English
made easy

Key Stage 2
ages 10–11
Workbook 1

Author
John Hesk

LONDON • NEW YORK • SYDNEY • DELHI

What's in a name?

The **origin** of a word is where it comes from. Look at the list of **origins** below, and match each with the correct day of the week. The first one has been done for you.
Remember: The days of the week are **proper nouns** and so begin with capital letters.

The day of Tiw ....Tiw's day........... ....Tuesday..........

The day of Thor ....

The day of Saturn ....

The day of Woden ....

Now use a **dictionary** to find the **origins** of the remaining days. ☐D

The day of ....

The day of ....

The day of ....

The months of the year also have interesting **origins**. Can you identify them from these clues?

The month named after the two-faced Roman god **Janus** is ....

The month named after **Maia**, the mother of the god Mercury, is ....

The two months named in honour of **Julius** and **Augustus** Caesar are

.... and ....

In the Roman calendar, the two months that used to be the **seventh** and **eighth** months until July and August were added before them are

.... and ....

Now list the remaining six months of the year with their **origins**. ☐D

F................... is named after ....

M................... is named after ....

A................... is named after ....

J................... is named after ....

N................... is named after ....

D................... is named after ....

Place names

The **names** of many places (cities, towns and villages) are interesting because they indicate the **origin** of the place. The **suffixes** below are found at the end of many place names. **Remember**: A **suffix** is a group of letters added to the end of a word.

-borough or **-burgh** means a walled town or castle in old English
-chester or **-cester** were Roman versions of **-borough** or **-burgh**
-ham means a pasture or meadow
-ford means a way across a shallow part of a river
-ton means town

Use an **atlas** or **map** of Britain to find **place names** with the same endings as those below. List as many as you can.

Edin**burgh**	Man**chester**	Hamil**ton**
....	....	....
....	....	....
....	....	....
....	....	....

Wrex**ham**	Bed**ford**
....	....
....	....
....	....
....	....

These names have easy-to-understand **suffixes**. Find other places with the same endings.

Shef**field**	Cam**bridge**
....	....
....	....
....	....
....	....

Now look at a map of **North America, Australia** or **New Zealand**. Can you find similar or identical **place names** to those above? Why do you think **places** have these **names**?

....

....

People's names

Throughout the world, people's **names** often have meanings that give us clues to the person's **origins**. Here are a few **first names** and their meanings.

David means beloved (Hebrew).

Helen means bright (Greek).

Fiona means fair (Gaelic).

Neil means champion (Irish).

Yasmin means the jasmine flower (Arabic).

Donald means world chief (Celtic).

Can you find the meaning of your own **first name**? You will probably need to use a **reference book**, such as a book of baby names.

....

Match these **first names** with their meanings or **origins**. One is already matched for you.

Mark	my fine one (Welsh)
Leroy	from the plant (English)
Mfanwy	from the Roman god Mars (Latin)
Homer	lion (Latin)
Miranda	to be admired (Latin)
Holly	angel messenger (English)
Angela	from the Ancient Greek poet (Greek)
Leo	the king (French)

Many **surnames** also indicate **origins**. Some names have **prefixes** or **suffixes** that have particular meanings. **Mac** or **Mc** is a Gaelic prefix meaning **son of**. The Irish prefix **O'** means **descended from**, and **-son** is a suffix meaning **son of**.

Can you work out what these **surnames** mean?

MacNeil ....

O'Neil ....

Neilson ....

More origins of names

Many people's **surnames** derive from (come from) jobs done by their ancestors.
For example: Baker means **one who bakes and sells bread. Shepherd** means **one who looks after sheep.** Find the **origins** of these **surnames.** D

Smith derives from ....

Archer derives from ....

Wright derives from ....

Thatcher derives from ....

Carpenter derives from ....

Tanner derives from ....

Bowman derives from ....

Fletcher derives from ....

Chandler derives from ....

Mason derives from ....

Sawyer derives from ....

Cartwright derives from ....

Goldsmith derives from ....

Wheelwright derives from ....

Arrowsmith derives from ....

Now put these fifteen **surnames** into **alphabetical order.**

....

....

....

Can you find the **origin** of your **surname** or **family name**? It may **originate** from a different country from the one you live in.

....

Romeo and Juliet

O Romeo, Romeo! wherefore art thou Romeo?
Deny thy father and refuse thy name;
Or, if thou wilt not, be but sworn my love,
And I'll no longer be a Capulet.

This quote was written by a famous sixteenth-century writer. Can you fill in the missing letters in the following paragraphs about the writer and his play *Romeo and Juliet*?
Many of the **proper nouns**, **pronouns** and **prepositions** are incomplete. (Unless you know the play well, it will help if you borrow a copy from a library.)
Remember: A **proper noun** is a specifically named person or thing.
A **pronoun** is used in the place of a **noun** to avoid repeating the **noun**.
A **preposition** is placed before a word to connect it to other words in a sentence.

W_ _ _ _ _ _ Shake_ _ _ _ _ _ wrote a play
called R_m_ _ _ and J_ _ _ _ _t. The pl_ _ is about
two young people f_ _ _ two feuding families called the
M_ _t_ _ _ _ _s and the _ _pul_ts.

The pl_ _ was probably written in about 1595,
more than four-hundred years ago. Nevertheless, the story
that i_ tells is still very popular, and i_ has been adapted
several times f_r the cinema.

Although S_ _ _ _ _ _ _ _ _ _ _ _ originally set
h_ _ story in V_r_n_ in Italy, film versions have been
set in places such as the U_ _ _ _ _ _ _tat_s.

As yo_ may know, the story has such a sad ending that, in
the nineteenth century, _t was changed so that _ _m_ _
and J_l_ _t lived to marry each other!

Rewrite the information above in your best **joined handwriting**. Continue on a separate sheet of paper. Then add some more information about this famous playwright. You may need to use **reference books** or a **computer** to find information.

....
....
....
....
....

A living language

The English language changes over time: **old words** disappear, and **new words** appear.

Change the following **old words** to **modern words** with the same meaning. The **old words** all come from the quote on page 6. ☐D

Instead of **wherefore** we now say ....

Instead of **art** we now say ....

Instead of **wilt** we now say ....

Instead of **thou** and **thy** we now say .... and ....

Here are some more words that have almost or completely gone out of use. Change them to **modern words** or **phrases** with similar meanings. ☐D

yonder means ....

hath means ....

whither means ....

unto means ....

whence means ....

forth means ....

hast means ....

thither means ....

shalt means ....

goest means ....

maketh means ....

quoth means ....

Now take a look at some **new words** or new ways of using older words. Can you use each of these words in a short sentence that shows how and where it is used?

fries ....

wheelie ....

cassette ....

trainers ....

surf (the Net) ....

log on ....

freebie ....

skateboard ....

cyberspace ....

Connectives

Here are some one-word **connectives**.

and	but	when	because
so	for	as	though

Choose a different one of these **connectives** to link each of the paired sentences below.
Remember: Connectives are words or phrases that link together different parts of a text.
Connectives that link sentences, clauses or parts of phrases are called **conjunctions**.

I fell over. I hurt my knee. ....

....

The game ended. The referee blew his whistle. ....

....

She couldn't ride her bike. It had a puncture. ....

....

I couldn't spell that word. I fetched the dictionary. ....

....

We arrived on time. The train was delayed. ....

....

Here are some **words** and **phrases** that can also be used as **connectives**.

also	however	this means	for example	as this

Fit the **connectives** above into the spaces in these three paragraphs.

Many kinds of words can be used to connect ideas in a piece of writing.
F__r e__ __ __ __ __ __, pronouns, adverbs, and conjunctions are all useful.

T__ __ __ __ __ __ __s that we can make our writing more varied and
more interesting to read. A__ __o, the words we choose can help us to make
our meaning clearer to our readers.

H__ __ __ __ __r, we should try not to use too many of these connectives
in a short piece, __s __ __ __s can make our sentences long and confusing.

Colons, semicolons and dashes

Punctuation can be used to connect groups of words. The **punctuation marks** that do this are: the **colon (:)**, the **semicolon (;)** and the **dash (–)**.

Read each sentence below, and write another sentence using the same **punctuation marks**. **Remember**:

- A **colon** is used to introduce a list, a quotation or a second clause that makes the first clause easier to understand. (A clause is a group of words with a verb in it.)
- A **semicolon** is used to link complete clauses that are too closely related to separate with a full stop.
  It can also be used to separate items in a list that already has commas in it.
- A **dash** can be used to separate a comment from the rest of a sentence. It makes a stronger break than a comma and is less formal than brackets.

Bring these things with you: a jumper, your swimsuit, your lunch and your bus fare.

....

....

It was Shakespeare's Juliet who asked: "What's in a name?"

....

The match was abandoned: rain poured down.

....

....

We had to stop playing; I went to Matt's house.

....

I bought a kilo of big, juicy apples; two large, ripe lemons; a grapefruit and a punnet of delicious, sweet-smelling strawberries.

....

....

....

The weather is lovely – wish you were here!

....

Punctuation practice

Practise your **punctuation** by rewriting this letter on a separate sheet of paper. You will need to add a variety of **punctuation marks**, change small letters to **capitals** and set out the letter properly.

3 main road
south town
hatsville
14 May

dear sarah,
im writing to let you know that well be coming home next monday weve had a great time wesley says good luck with the show weve got you a surprise but he says im not to tell you anything about it youll just have to wait see you soon love from sophie

Now complete this guide to the use of **punctuation**.

How to Use Punctuation

Full stops are used at the end of a...

Apostrophes are used ....

and ....

Commas are used ....

....

Capital letters are needed for ....

....

Speech marks are placed around ....

....

Question marks are placed ....

....

Exclamation marks show ....

....

Colons, semicolons and **dashes** are used to ....

....

Active and passive

Active sentences describe an action done **by the subject**.
  I directed the award-winning film. (an **active** sentence)
Passive sentences describe an action done **to the subject**.
  The award-winning film was directed by me. (a **passive** sentence)

Change these sentences from **passive** to **active**.

The match was won by our team.

Our team ....

The winning goal was scored by Rachel.

....

The party was enjoyed by all my friends.

Jack was stung by an unusual insect.

....

Now change these sentences from **active** to **passive**.

Aliens invade our planet.

Our planet is ....

Leonardo da Vinci painted the *Mona Lisa*.

....

The team dislike the group leader.

....

The hero piloted his craft with great skill.

....

A hurricane struck the town.

....

Reading a poem

Read this **poem** aloud.

My brother

my brother's on the floor roaring
my brother's on the floor roaring
why is my brother on the floor roaring?
my brother is on the floor roaring
because he's supposed to finish his beans
before he has his pudding

but he doesn't want to finish his beans
before he has his pudding

he says he wants his pudding
NOW

but they won't let him

so now my brother is on the floor roaring

they're saying
I give you one more chance to finish those beans
or you don't go to Tony's
but he's not listening
because he's on the floor roaring

he's getting told off
I'm not
I've eaten my beans
and do you know what I'm doing now?
I'm eating my pudding
and he's on the floor roaring

if he wasn't on the floor roaring
he'd see me eating my pudding
if he looked really close
he might see a little tiny smile
just at the corner of my mouth
but he's not looking
he's on the floor roaring

the pudding is OK
it's not wonderful
not wonderful enough
to be sitting on the floor and roaring about –
unless you're my brother

Michael Rosen

Reading and understanding

Answer these questions about the **poem** on page 12.

What do you notice about the **punctuation** in this poem? Give reasons for your answer.

....

....

Who do you think is the **narrator** in this poem? What sort of person might he or she be?

....

....

How do you think the narrator feels about his or her brother's behaviour? Can you find any evidence for what you think?

....

....

Count the number of times the poet uses the word **roaring**. By repeating this word so often, is the effect of the poem spoiled or improved? Give reasons for your answer.

....

....

Who are "they" in this poem?

....

Try **punctuating** this part of the poem as if it were part of a **story**.
    they're saying
    I give you one more chance to finish those beans
    or you don't go to Tony's

....

....

....

Retelling the story from another angle.
Retell the **story** as if you were either the brother who is roaring or one of the parents. You'll need to imagine what happens before and after the poem. Write your **story** in the **first person** (use **I**, **my**, **we**, etc.), and think of a new **title** for your **retelling**. **Plan** your **story** by writing brief **notes**. Write your **notes** and **story** on separate pieces of paper.

Reading a classic novel

Charlotte Brontë wrote her novel *Jane Eyre* in 1847. The main character, Jane, is an orphan sent away to a boarding school by her cruel aunt. The school for orphaned girls is run by a charity and has many strict rules and regulations. The girls are poorly clothed and fed. Only one teacher, Miss Temple the superintendent, is kind and sympathetic.

Read these three **extracts** from the book.

… the classes were marshalled and marched into another room to breakfast. How glad I was to behold the prospect of getting something to eat!

The refectory was a great, low-ceiled, gloomy room. On two long tables smoked basins of something hot, which, however, to my dismay, sent forth an odour far from inviting.

… from the van of the procession, the tall girls of the first class, rose the whispered words, –

"Disgusting! The porridge is burnt again!"

Ravenous, and now very faint, I devoured a spoonful or two of my portion without thinking of its taste; but the first edge of hunger blunted, I perceived I had got in hand a nauseous mess: burnt porridge is almost as bad as rotten potatoes; … The spoons were moved slowly: I saw each girl taste her food and try to swallow it; but in most cases the effort was soon relinquished. Breakfast was over, and none had breakfasted. …

The duration of each lesson was measured by the clock, which at last struck twelve. The superintendent rose.

…"You had this morning a breakfast which you could not eat; you must be hungry:– I have ordered that a lunch of bread and cheese shall be served to all."

The teachers looked at her with a sort of surprise.

"It is to be done on my responsibility," she added, in an explanatory tone to them, and immediately afterwards left the room. The bread and cheese was presently brought in and distributed, to the high delight and refreshment of the whole school.

… the summons sounded for dinner; all re-entered the house. The odour which now filled the refectory was scarcely more appetizing than that which had regaled our nostrils at breakfast: the dinner was served in two huge tin-plated vessels, whence rose a strong steam redolent of rancid fat. I found the mess to consist of indifferent potatoes and strange shreds of rusty meat, mixed and cooked together. Of this preparation a tolerably abundant plateful was apportioned to each pupil. I ate what I could, and wondered within myself whether every day's fare would be like this.

Reading and understanding

Use a **dictionary** or **thesaurus** to find a suitable word or phrase that could replace each of the following words from the **extract** on page 14 without changing its meaning. [D] [T]

marshalled ....

odour ....

relinquished ....

redolent ....

apportioned ....

vessels ....

refectory ....

ravenous ....

regaled ....

abundant ....

fare ....

van ....

Why did Jane **devour** the first spoonful of porridge? [D]

....

The porridge made Jane feel **nauseous**. Describe this feeling in your own words. [D]

....

Why were the girls so glad to have bread and cheese for lunch?

....

Would you have enjoyed the dinner? Give reasons for your answer.

....

Find a sentence with a **passive verb** in it. Write it here.
Remember: Passive verbs describe an action done to the subject (not by the subject).

....

....

Find a sentence with an **active verb** in it. Write it here.
Remember: Active verbs describe an action done by the subject (not to the subject).

....

....

Reading a modern text

Read this **description** of a Norwegian family feast, then answer the questions.

 This was a Norwegian household, and for the Norwegians the best food in the world is fish. And when they say fish, they don't mean the sort of thing you and I get from the fishmonger. They mean *fresh fish*, fish that has been caught no more than twenty-four hours before and has never been frozen or chilled on a block of ice. I agree with them that the proper way to prepare fish like this is to poach it, and that is what they do with the finest specimens. And Norwegians, by the way, always eat the skin of the boiled fish, which they say has the best taste of all.

So naturally this great celebration feast started with fish. A massive fish, a flounder as big as a tea-tray and as thick as your arm was brought to the table. It had nearly black skin on top which was covered with brilliant orange spots, and it had, of course, been perfectly poached. Large white hunks of this fish were carved out and put on to our plates, and with it we had hollandaise sauce and boiled new potatoes. Nothing else. And by gosh, it was delicious.

As soon as the remains of the fish had been cleared away, a tremendous craggy mountain of home-made ice-cream would be carried in. Apart from being the creamiest ice-cream in the world, the flavour was unforgettable. There were thousands of little chips of crisp burnt toffee mixed into it (the Norwegians call it *krokan*), and as a result it didn't simply melt in your mouth like ordinary ice-cream. You chewed it and it went *crunch* and the taste was something you dreamed about for days afterwards.

From *Boy, Tales of Childhood* by Roald Dahl

What is the writer's **definition** of fresh fish?

....

....

Write down the two **similes** used by the writer to give us an idea of the size of the fish.
Remember: A **simile** is something compared with something else to create an image in the reader's mind. It usually includes the words **like** or **as**.

....

Write down the **metaphor** used by Roald Dahl in his **description** of the ice-cream.
Remember: A **metaphor** is something described as if it were something else.

....

Do you think these descriptions of the fish and the ice-cream are factual or exaggerated? Give reasons for your answer.

....

....

Answer Section with Parents' Notes

Key Stage 2
Ages 10–11
Workbook 1

This 8-page section provides answers or explanatory notes to all the activities in this book. This will enable you to assess your child's work.

Point out any spelling mistakes, incorrect punctuation and grammatical errors as you mark each page. Also correct any handwriting errors. (Your child should use the handwriting style taught at his or her school.) As well as making corrections, it is very important to praise your child's efforts and achievements.

Encourage your child to use a dictionary, and suggest that he or she uses a notebook to compile a **word bank** of new words or difficult spellings.

---

2 ⭐ What's in a name?

The **origin** of a word is where it comes from. Look at the list of **origins** below, and match each with the correct day of the week. The first one has been done for you.
Remember: The days of the week are **proper nouns** and so begin with capital letters.

The day of Tiw	Tiw's day	Tuesday
The day of Thor	Thor's day	Thursday
The day of Saturn	Saturn's day	Saturday
The day of Woden	Woden's day	Wednesday

Now use a **dictionary** to find the **origins** of the remaining days. [D]

The day of the Sun	Sun's day	Sunday
The day of the Moon	Moon's day	Monday
The day of Frigg	Frigg's day	Friday

The months of the year also have interesting **origins**. Can you identify them from these clues?

The month named after the two-faced Roman god **Janus** is January

The month named after **Maia**, the mother of the god Mercury, is May

The two months named in honour of **Julius** and **Augustus** Caesar are
July and August

In the Roman calendar, the two months that used to be the **seventh** and **eighth** months until July and August were added before them are
September and October

Now list the remaining six months of the year with their **origins**. [D]

F ebruary	is named after	februa, the Roman purification festival.
M arch	is named after	the Roman god Mars.
A pril	is named after	the Latin word for opening or Spring.
J une	is named after	the Roman goddess Juno.
N ovember	is named after	the ninth month in the old calendar.
D ecember	is named after	the tenth month in the old calendar.

On this page, the task is to research the origins and meanings of everyday names. This will help your child to extend his or her vocabulary and to develop an interest in the history of English. Help your child to look up the words in a dictionary.

---

3 Place names ⭐

The **names** of many places (cities, towns and villages) are interesting because they indicate the **origin** of the place. The **suffixes** below are found at the end of many place names.
Remember: A suffix is a group of letters added to the end of a word.

-**borough** or -**burgh** means a walled town or castle in old English
-**chester** or -**cester** were Roman versions of -**borough** or -**burgh**
-**ham** means a pasture or meadow
-**ford** means a way across a shallow part of a river
-**ton** means town

Use an **atlas** or **map** of Britain to find **place names** with the same endings as those below. List as many as you can.

| Edin**burgh** | Man**chester** | Hamil**ton** |

Answers may vary

| Wrex**ham** | Bed**ford** |

These names have easy-to-understand **suffixes**. Find other places with the same endings.

| Shef**field** | Cam**bridge** |

Now look at a map of **North America**, **Australia** or **New Zealand**. Can you find similar or identical **place names** to those above? Why do you think **places** have these **names**?
Places in America, Australia and New Zealand were often named after the home towns of the first British people who settled there.

This exercise offers practice in using an atlas or map as a reference tool. Any place names with the specified endings are acceptable answers. Your child may also be able to tell you which endings are of Roman, Saxon, or Viking origin.

---

4 ⭐ People's names

Throughout the world, people's **names** often have meanings that give us clues to the person's **origins**. Here are a few **first names** and their meanings.

David means beloved (Hebrew).

Helen means bright (Greek).

Fiona means fair (Gaelic).

Neil means champion (Irish).

Yasmin means the jasmine flower (Arabic).

Donald means world chief (Celtic).

Can you find the meaning of your own **first name**? You will probably need to use a **reference book**, such as a book of baby names.
Answers may vary

Match these **first names** with their meanings or **origins**. One is already matched for you.

Mark — from the Roman god Mars (Latin)
Leroy — the king (French)
Mfanwy — my fine one (Welsh)
Homer — from the Ancient Greek poet (Greek)
Miranda — to be admired (Latin)
Holly — from the plant (English)
Angela — angel messenger (English)
Leo — lion (Latin)

Many **surnames** also indicate **origins**. Some names have **prefixes** or **suffixes** that have particular meanings. **Mac** or **Mc** is a Gaelic prefix meaning **son of**. The Irish prefix **O'** means **descended from**, and -**son** is a suffix meaning **son of**.

Can you work out what these **surnames** mean?
MacNeil son of Neil
O'Neil descended from Neil
Neilson son of Neil

This page gives your child further practice in researching the meanings of names. If your own dictionary does not list the origins of names, you may need to visit a local library to find a dictionary of names or a baby-naming book.

5 — More origins of names

Many people's **surnames** derive from (come from) jobs done by their ancestors. **For example: Baker** means **one who bakes and sells bread. Shepherd** means **one who looks after sheep.** Find the **origins** of these **surnames.**   D

Smith derives from _a person who works with metal._

Archer derives from _a person skilled in the use of the bow and arrow._

Wright derives from _a person who creates, builds or repairs._

Thatcher derives from _a person who makes and repairs thatched roofs._

Carpenter derives from _a person who works with wood._

Tanner derives from _a person who treats animal skins to make leather._

Bowman derives from _a person who uses a bow and arrow._

Fletcher derives from _a person who makes arrows._

Chandler derives from _a person who makes or sells candles._

Mason derives from _a person who works with stone._

Sawyer derives from _a person who saws timber._

Cartwright derives from _a person who makes carts._

Goldsmith derives from _a person who works with gold._

Wheelwright derives from _a person who makes wheels._

Arrowsmith derives from _a person who makes arrows._

Now put these fifteen **surnames** into **alphabetical order.**
Archer, Arrowsmith, Bowman, Carpenter, Cartwright, Chandler, Fletcher,
Goldsmith, Mason, Sawyer, Smith, Tanner, Thatcher, Wheelwright, Wright

Can you find the **origin** of your **surname** or **family name**? It may **originate** from a different country from the one you live in.

On this page your child will explore the meanings of surnames. You may need to help your child research his or her family name at a local library. If you are unable to find a definite origin for your child's surname, explain that this is not unusual.

6 — Romeo and Juliet

O Romeo, Romeo! wherefore art thou Romeo!
Deny thy father and refuse thy name;
Or, if thou wilt not, be but sworn my love,
And I'll no longer be a Capulet.

This quote was written by a famous sixteenth-century writer. Can you fill in the missing letters in the following paragraphs about the writer and his play *Romeo and Juliet*? Many of the **proper nouns, pronouns** and **prepositions** are incomplete. (Unless you know the play well, it will help if you borrow a copy from a library.)
Remember: A **proper noun** is a specifically named person or thing.
A **pronoun** is used in the place of a **noun** to avoid repeating the **noun.**
A **preposition** is placed before a word to connect it to other words in a sentence.

W i l l i a m Shakespeare wrote a play called R o m e o and J u l i e t. The pl a y is about two young people f r o m two feuding families called the M o n t a g u e s and the C a p u l e ts.

The pl a y was probably written in about 1595, more than four-hundred years ago. Nevertheless, the story that i t tells is still very popular, and i t has been adapted several times f o r the cinema.

Although S h a k e s p e a r e originally set h i s story in V e r o n a in Italy, film versions have been set in places such as the U n i t e d s t a t e s.

As yo u may know, the story has such a sad ending that, in the nineteenth century, i t was changed so that R o m e o and J u l i e t lived to marry each other!

Rewrite the information above in your best **joined handwriting.** Continue on a separate sheet of paper. Then add some more information about this famous playwright. You may need to use **reference books** or a **computer** to find information.

Answers may vary

Your child may be studying one or more of Shakespeare's plays at school. These activities help practise the use of proper nouns, pronouns and prepositions. At this key stage, handwriting is expected to be joined, fluent and legible.

7 — A living language

The English language changes over time: **old words** disappear, and **new words** appear.

Change the following **old words** to **modern words** with the same meaning. The **old words** all come from the quote on page 6.   D

Instead of **wherefore** we now say _why_

Instead of **art** we now say _are_

Instead of **wilt** we now say _will_

Instead of **thou** and **thy** we now say _you_ and _your_

Here are some more words that have almost or completely gone out of use. Change them to **modern words** or **phrases** with similar meanings.   D

yonder means _over there_   hast means _have_

hath means _has_   thither means _to there_

whither means _to where_   shalt means _shall_

unto means _to_   goest means _go_

whence means _from where_   maketh means _make_

forth means _forward_   quoth means _said_

Now take a look at some **new words** or new ways of using older words. Can you use each of these words in a short sentence that shows how and where it is used?

fries ....

wheelie ....

cassette ....

trainers ....

surf (the Net) ....

log on ....

freebie ....

skateboard ....

cyberspace ....

The exercises on this page will help your child to appreciate how language changes over time. Emphasise that old words often resemble modern ones. In the final section, accept any sentences that use the words correctly.

8 — Connectives

Here are some one-word **connectives.**

| and | but | when | because |
| so | for | as | though |

Choose a different one of these **connectives** to link each of the paired sentences below.
Remember: Connectives are words or phrases that link together different parts of a text. **Connectives** that link sentences, clauses or parts of phrases are called **conjunctions.**

I fell over. I hurt my knee. _I fell over and I hurt my knee._

The game ended. The referee blew his whistle. _The game ended when the referee blew his whistle._

She couldn't ride her bike. It had a puncture. _She couldn't ride her bike because it had a puncture._

I couldn't spell that word. I fetched the dictionary. _I couldn't spell that word so I fetched the dictionary._

We arrived on time. The train was delayed. _We arrived on time but the train was delayed._

Here are some **words** and **phrases** that can also be used as **connectives.**

| also | however | this means | for example | as this |

Fit the **connectives** above into the spaces in these three paragraphs.

Many kinds of words can be used to connect ideas in a piece of writing. F o r e x a m p l e, pronouns, adverbs and conjunctions are all useful.

T h i s m e a n s that we can make our writing more varied and more interesting to read. A l s o, the words we choose can help us to make our meaning clearer to our readers.

H o w e v e r, we should try not to use too many of these connectives in a short piece, a s t h i s can make our sentences long and confusing.

Here your child practises using connectives (joining words, phrases or clauses). As your child works through the final exercise, check that he or she understands the meaning of the passage. Don't forget to praise your child's efforts.

Colons, semicolons and dashes

Punctuation can be used to connect groups of words. The **punctuation marks** that do this are: the **colon** (:), the **semicolon** (;) and the **dash** (–).

Read each sentence below, and write another sentence using the same **punctuation marks**. **Remember**:
- A **colon** is used to introduce a list, a quotation or a second clause that makes the first clause easier to understand. (A clause is a group of words with a verb in it.)
- A **semicolon** is used to link complete clauses that are too closely related to separate with a full stop.
  It can also be used to separate items in a list that already has commas in it.
- A **dash** can be used to separate a comment from the rest of a sentence. It makes a stronger break than a comma and is less formal than brackets.

Bring these things with you: a jumper, your swimsuit, your lunch and your bus fare.

....

....

It was Shakespeare's Juliet who asked: "What's in a name?"

....

The match was abandoned: rain poured down.

....

....

We had to stop playing: I went to Matt's house.

....

I bought a kilo of big, juicy apples; two large, ripe lemons; a grapefruit and a punnet of delicious, sweet-smelling strawberries.

....

....

....

The weather is lovely – wish you were here!

....

(watermark: Answers may vary)

These sentences help your child explore the use of colons, semicolons and dashes. Children often find these sophisticated punctuation marks very difficult to use, so you may need to offer help. Accept any sentences with the correct punctuation.

Punctuation practice

Practise your **punctuation** by rewriting this letter on a separate sheet of paper. You will need to add a variety of **punctuation marks**, change small letters to **capitals** and set out the letter properly.

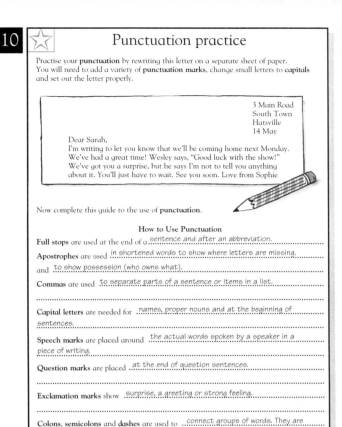

> 3 Main Road
> South Town
> Hatsville
> 14 May
>
> Dear Sarah,
> I'm writing to let you know that we'll be coming home next Monday. We've had a great time! Wesley says, "Good luck with the show!" We've got you a surprise, but he says I'm not to tell you anything about it. You'll just have to wait. See you soon. Love from Sophie

Now complete this guide to the use of **punctuation**.

How to Use Punctuation

Full stops are used at the end of a *sentence and after an abbreviation.*

Apostrophes are used *in shortened words to show where letters are missing.* and *to show possession (who owns what).*

Commas are used *to separate parts of a sentence or items in a list.*

Capital letters are needed for *names, proper nouns and at the beginning of sentences.*

Speech marks are placed around *the actual words spoken by a speaker in a piece of writing.*

Question marks are placed *at the end of question sentences.*

Exclamation marks show *surprise, a greeting or strong feeling.*

Colons, semicolons and **dashes** are used to *connect groups of words. They are stronger than commas.*

On this page your child revises and practises punctuation. Check that the letter is laid out and punctuated correctly. In the second exercise, accept any answers that explain the correct use of a punctuation mark.

Active and passive

Active sentences describe an action done **by the subject**.
    I directed the award-winning film. (an **active** sentence)
Passive sentences describe an action done **to the subject**.
    The award-winning film was directed by me. (a **passive** sentence)

Change these sentences from **passive** to **active**.

The match was won by our team.
Our team won the match.

The winning goal was scored by Rachel.
Rachel scored the winning goal.

The party was enjoyed by all my friends.
All my friends enjoyed the party.

Jack was stung by an unusual insect.
An unusual insect stung Jack.

Now change these sentences from **active** to **passive**.

Aliens invade our planet.
Our planet is invaded by aliens.

Leonardo da Vinci painted the *Mona Lisa*.
The Mona Lisa was painted by Leonardo da Vinci.

The team dislike the group leader.
The group leader is disliked by the team.

The hero piloted his craft with great skill.
The hero's craft was piloted with great skill.

A hurricane struck the town.
The town was struck by a hurricane.

Here the task is to change a sentence from active to passive and *vice versa*. Check that your child understands the difference between the active and passive voices and can use them confidently. It may help if you think up practice sentences together.

Reading a poem

Read this **poem** aloud.

My brother

my brother's on the floor roaring
my brother's on the floor roaring
why is my brother on the floor roaring?
my brother is on the floor roaring
because he's supposed to finish his beans
before he has his pudding

but he doesn't want to finish his beans
before he has his pudding

he says he wants his pudding
NOW

but they won't let him

so now my brother is on the floor roaring

they're saying
I give you one more chance to finish those beans
or you don't go to Tony's
but he's not listening
because he's on the floor roaring

he's getting told off
I'm not
I've eaten my beans
and do you know what I'm doing now?
I'm eating my pudding
and he's on the floor roaring

if he wasn't on the floor roaring
he'd see me eating my pudding
if he looked really close
he might see a little tiny smile
just at the corner of my mouth
but he's not looking
he's on the floor roaring

the pudding is OK
it's not wonderful
not wonderful enough
to be sitting on the floor and roaring about –
unless you're my brother

Michael Rosen

This poem appeals to children's experience of everyday life by adopting both the voice and viewpoint of a child. Encourage your child to read the poem aloud or, if he or she needs more help, you could read it together.

Reading and understanding

Answer these questions about the **poem** on page 12.

What do you notice about the **punctuation** in this poem? Give reasons for your answer.
There is almost no punctuation in this poem. It could be because the narrator is
thinking in a continuous "stream".

Who do you think is the **narrator** in this poem? What sort of person might he or she be?
The narrator is either the older brother or the older sister of the child in the
poem. He or she feels superior to the boy on the floor.

How do you think the narrator feels about his or her brother's behaviour? Can you find
any evidence for what you think?
He or she thinks that the younger brother is silly because he or she doesn't think
the pudding is worth such a fuss.

Count the number of times the poet uses the word **roaring**. By repeating this word
so often, is the effect of the poem spoiled or improved? Give reasons for your answer.
The word "roaring" is used 10 times. It improves the poem because it emphasises
what a huge fuss the brother is making.

Who are "they" in this poem?
"They" in this poem are adults, probably the children's parents.

Try **punctuating** this part of the poem as if it were part of a **story**.
  they're saying
  I give you one more chance to finish those beans
  or you don't go to Tony's

They're saying, "I give you one more chance to finish those beans or you don't go
to Tony's!"

Retelling the story from another angle.
Retell the **story** as if you were either the brother who is roaring or one of the parents.
You'll need to imagine what happens before and after the poem. Write your **story** in the
first person (use **I, my, we**, etc.), and think of a new **title** for your **retelling**. **Plan** your
story by writing brief **notes**. Write your **notes** and **story** on separate pieces of paper.

Here, your child analyses the different viewpoints
of characters in a poem. Talk to your child about
how the other characters might view the events.
Remember to tell your child what you like about
his or her retelling of the story.

Reading a classic novel

Charlotte Brontë wrote her novel *Jane Eyre* in 1847. The main character, Jane, is an
orphan sent away to a boarding school by her cruel aunt. The school for orphaned girls
is run by a charity and has many strict rules and regulations. The girls are poorly clothed
and fed. Only one teacher, Miss Temple the superintendent, is kind and sympathetic.

Read these three **extracts** from the book.

… the classes were marshalled and marched into
another room to breakfast. How glad I was to behold
the prospect of getting something to eat!
  The refectory was a great, low-ceiled, gloomy room.
On two long tables smoked basins of something hot, which,
however, to my dismay, sent forth an odour far from inviting.
  … from the van of the procession, the tall girls of the first
class, rose the whispered words, –
  "Disgusting! The porridge is burnt again!"
Ravenous, and now very faint, I devoured a spoonful or two of my portion without
thinking of its taste; but the first edge of hunger blunted, I perceived I had got in hand
a nauseous mess: burnt porridge is almost as bad as rotten potatoes; … The spoons were
moved slowly: I saw each girl taste her food and try to swallow it; but in most cases the
effort was soon relinquished. Breakfast was over, and none had breakfasted. …

The duration of each lesson was measured by the clock,
which at last struck twelve. The superintendent rose.
  …"You had this morning a breakfast which you could
not eat; you must be hungry:– I have ordered that a lunch
of bread and cheese shall be served to all."
  The teachers looked at her with a sort of surprise.
  "It is to be done on my responsibility," she added, in an
explanatory tone to them, and immediately afterwards left
the room. The bread and cheese was presently brought in
and distributed, to the high delight and refreshment of the
whole school.

… the summons sounded for dinner; all re-entered the house. The odour which now
filled the refectory was scarcely more appetizing than that which had regaled our nostrils
at breakfast: the dinner was served in two huge tin-plated vessels, whence rose a strong
steam redolent of rancid fat. I found the mess to consist of indifferent potatoes and
strange shreds of rusty meat, mixed and cooked together. Of this preparation a tolerably
abundant plateful was apportioned to each pupil. I ate what I could, and wondered
within myself whether every day's fare would be like this.

Read through the passage with your child. You
could point out that, although it is written in the
first person and is based on the author's own
experience, *Jane Eyre* is a fictional autobiography.
(This point comes up again on page 18.)

Reading and understanding

Use a **dictionary** or **thesaurus** to find a suitable word or phrase that could replace each of
the following words from the **extract** on page 14 without changing its meaning. D T

marshalled	lined up	refectory	dining hall
odour	smell	ravenous	very hungry
relinquished	given up	regaled	delighted
redolent	smelling	abundant	plentiful
apportioned	shared out	fare	meals
vessels	containers	van	front

Why did Jane **devour** the first spoonful of porridge? D
Jane devoured the first spoonful of porridge because she was very hungry.

The porridge made Jane feel **nauseous**. Describe this feeling in your own words. D
Nauseous means feeling like you might be sick.

Why were the girls so glad to have bread and cheese for lunch?
The girls were hungry and they knew that the bread and cheese would be edible.

Would you have enjoyed the dinner? Give reasons for your answer.
Answers may vary

Find a sentence with a **passive verb** in it. Write it here.
Remember: Passive verbs describe an action done to the subject (not by the subject).
Answers may vary

Find a sentence with an **active verb** in it. Write it here.
Remember: Active verbs describe an action done by the subject (not to the subject).
Answers may vary

These activities encourage your child to imagine
himself or herself in a fictional character's
situation. Several of the questions are meant to be
speculative and open-ended. Any answer that is
sensibly argued is acceptable.

Reading a modern text

Read this **description** of a Norwegian family feast, then answer the questions.

 This was a Norwegian household, and for the Norwegians the best
food in the world is fish. And when they say fish, they don't mean
the sort of thing you and I get from the fishmonger. They mean
fresh fish, fish that has been caught no more than twenty-four hours
before and has never been frozen or chilled on a block of ice. I agree with them that the
proper way to prepare fish like this is to poach it, and that is what they do with the finest
specimens. And Norwegians, by the way, always eat the skin of the boiled fish, which
they say has the best taste of all.
  So naturally this great celebration feast started with fish. A massive fish, a flounder
as big as a tea-tray and as thick as your arm was brought to the table. It had nearly
black skin on top which was covered with brilliant orange spots, and it had, of course,
been perfectly poached. Large white hunks of this fish were carved out and put on to
our plates, and with it we had hollandaise sauce and boiled new potatoes. Nothing else.
And by gosh, it was delicious.
  As soon as the remains of the fish had been cleared away, a tremendous craggy
mountain of home-made ice-cream would be carried in. Apart from being the creamiest
ice-cream in the world, the flavour was unforgettable. There were thousands of little
chips of crisp burnt toffee mixed into it (the Norwegians call it *krokan*), and as a result
it didn't simply melt in your mouth like ordinary ice-cream. You chewed it and it went
crunch and the taste was something you dreamed about for days afterwards.

From Boy, Tales of Childhood by Roald Dahl

What is the writer's **definition** of fresh fish?
Fresh fish is fish that has been caught no more than twenty-four hours
before and has never been frozen or chilled on a block of ice.

Write down the two **similes** used by the writer to give us an idea of the size of the fish.
Remember: A **simile** is something compared with something else to create an image in
the reader's mind. It usually includes the words **like** or **as**.
as big as a tea-tray and as thick as your arm

Write down the **metaphor** used by Roald Dahl in his **description** of the ice-cream.
Remember: A **metaphor** is something described as if it were something else.
a tremendous craggy mountain.

Do you think these descriptions of the fish and the ice-cream are factual or exaggerated?
Give reasons for your answer.
Answers may vary

This page and the following one give your child
practice in recognising the elements of style and
theme shared by two texts written by the same
author. Check that your child writes his or her
answers in complete sentences.

A writer's style ☆

Read the following **description**, then answer the questions.

> ... I can remember exactly what was on the table that evening. It was my favourite thing of all, toad-in-the-hole, and my mum could make toad-in-the-hole like nobody else in the world. She did it in an enormous pan with the Yorkshire pudding very brown and crisp on top and raised up in huge bubbly mountains. In between the mountains you could see the sausages half-buried in the batter. Fantastic it was.
>
> From *Danny, Champion of the World* by Roald Dahl

What is **toad-in-the-hole**? Why do you think the writer chose this type of meal? D
Toad-in-the-hole is a dish of sausages baked in batter. The author chose this meal as it is the type of meal a young boy would like.

Make a list of the **exaggerated expressions** used in this description.
I can remember exactly, like nobody else in the world, enormous pan, huge bubbly mountains. Fantastic.

Can you find a **metaphor** that reminds you of the Norwegian feast on page 16?
huge bubbly mountains

How might you know that Roald Dahl wrote this? Look at the **style** of writing, and compare it with the **style** of the text on page 16.
Remember: An author's **style** is the particular way in which he or she writes.
Both descriptions are of food. They are written in a similar style with exaggerated expressions, metaphors and similes.

These questions give further practice in spotting the common elements of style in two passages by the same author. To prepare for the questions on page 18, talk to your child about whether this passage is biographical or autobiographical.

Fact or fiction?

Find these words in a **dictionary**, then write your own **definition** of each. D
biography the life story of a person written by someone else.
autobiography the life story of a person written by that person.

Look back at page 14. Is *Jane Eyre* a **factual** or **fictional autobiography**? Give a reason for your answer.
Jane Eyre is a fictional autobiography; it is written as if Jane herself was telling the story, but it was really written by Charlotte Brontë.

Is *Jane Eyre* written in the **first person** (using **I/we**) or the **third person** (using **she/they**)?
Jane Eyre is written in the first person.

Do you think the **description** on page 16 is from a **factual** or **fictional autobiography**? Give a reason for your answer.
The description on page 16 is from a factual autobiography. The title is down to earth and the writing is vivid, which makes me think it is describing a real meal.

How would you describe your writing about Shakespeare on page 6?
Biographical

Write your own **description** of your favourite meal (either real or imaginary) as Roald Dahl might have written it. First, reread the texts on pages 16 and 17 to get a feel for Dahl's **style**, then use this menu card as a **plan**.

> M E N U
>
> Starter: ....
>
> Main course: ....
>
> Dessert: ....

Answers may vary

Now write the **description** on a separate sheet of paper. Try to use the same **style** as Roald Dahl, but use your own **similes** and **metaphors**.

Here the menu provides a structure for your child's description, which should contain some of the stylistic elements identified on pages 16 and 17. Encourage your child to have fun by playing with exaggeration, metaphors and similes.

Limericks

Read the following **limericks**, then answer the questions.

1 Asks Paolo, when peckish, in Pisa,
"Spaghetti and sauce – what is eas*ia*?"
Each evening at eight
He sits down to a plate
Of the most perfect pasta in Pisa.

2 Now, Mamie and Max from Manhattan
Think doughnuts are great – but they fatten!
All sticky and sweet,
Only bought for a treat,
Just the food for a "mood" in Manhattan.

3 Dolores, down Mexico way,
Likes chilli con carne each day.
That the chillis are hot!
Troubles her not one jot!
She just chooses her chilli that way.

Glenis Hesk

Do you know why poems like these are called **limericks**? Try to find out, then look at the **limericks** above to help you complete this **definition**. D

A limerick is a comic verse that always has f i v e lines. The longer lines, which are lines one, t w o and f i v e , rhyme with each other. The s h o r t e r lines, three and f o u r , share a different rhyme. This rhyme **pattern**, or rhyme **scheme**, is known as A, A, B, B, A.

How many examples of **alliteration** can you find in the first **limerick**? 4
Can you explain the meaning of **alliteration**?
Alliteration is where words that are next to each other or close to each other begin with the same sound.

Write the words that **alliterate** in the second and the third limericks.
Mamie, Max, Manhattan; sticky, sweet; mood, Manhattan; con, carne; chooses, chilli

Which extra two **rhyming words** in the second **limerick** are not in the expected place at the ends of the lines?
food and mood

Did you notice the "funny" spelling in the first **limerick**? Why do you think it is there?
"Easia" should really be spelt "easier", but it was spelt this way to rhyme with "Pisa".

What does the saying "not one jot" mean?
"Not one jot" means "not at all".

Here your child learns to recognise limericks and the stylistic device of alliteration. Encourage your child to read the limericks out loud. Point out to your child that the first line of a limerick usually introduces a person and a place.

Alliteration

Write down any four words that **alliterate** with **chooses** and **chilli**.
Remember: Alliteration is when two or more words close to each other in a piece of writing begin with the same sound.

....

Now write down **two** words that **alliterate** with each of the following words. Use the sound made by the **two** letters at the beginning of the words.

what	....	think	....
treat	....	sticky	....
sweet	....	fleet	....
brand	....	flavour	....
shoulder	....	phantom	....
quarter	....	wrinkle	....

Answers may vary

Now use the sound of the **three** letters at the beginning of each of these words to write **three** more words that **alliterate** with each one.

thread ....

stranger ....

splendid ....

sprout ....

scramble ....

squash ....

chrome ....

This page explores the concept of alliteration in more detail and provides practice with the spelling of common strings of letters. Encourage your child to use a dictionary to find and check the spelling of the alliterating words.

Writing limericks

Try writing some **limericks** of your own on any **subject** or **theme**. Use what you have learned on pages 19 and 20 to help you. Remember to make your limericks **amusing**.

....

....

....

....

....

....

....

....

....

....

....

....

....

....

....

....

....

On this page, the task is for your child to write his or her own limericks, which should follow the pattern given on page 19. Encourage your child to have fun with this exercise. There is no need to fill the whole page.

Reading and understanding

Although pirates in stories are often portrayed as lovable rogues, the real-life pirates who sailed the oceans searching out laden ships were usually ruthless robbers. Read the following **historical information** about real pirates.

The Bahamas pirates became so cocksure that in 1718, when the British government sent a fleet of ships to clear the islands of piracy, one of them – Charles Vane – sailed down the line of naval vessels saluting each one.

That same year, however, a new governor arrived who at last succeeded in clearing the Bahamas of pirates. He was Woodes Rogers, originally a merchant from Bristol, and himself a former pirate. Between 1708 and 1711 Rogers made a privateering voyage to make up for the losses he had suffered when pirates seized his ships. Rogers looted the Spanish colony at Guayaquil, Ecuador, where he stole a fortune in silver and valuables. On his way home to England he captured a Spanish galleon with treasure on board worth £1 million.

As governor, Rogers dealt with the Bahamas pirates by first offering them a pardon. Some accepted. Those who did not were very severely dealt with. In November 1718 Rogers had three captured pirates put on trial, followed by ten more in December.

From then on the 2,000 pirates still at large in the Caribbean avoided the Bahamas. As for Charles Vane, he accepted the pardon Rogers offered, but wanted to keep all his ill-gotten gains. When Rogers refused, Vane hoisted the "Jolly Roger," fired one last defiant salvo, and sailed away. He was never seen in the Bahamas again.

From *World History* by Brenda Ralph Lewis

Now **summarise** (write a shortened version of) this extract. Use a separate sheet of paper, and try to write no more than 80 words. Here are some guidelines to help you.

1 Read the first sentence, think about it, then read the last sentence.
2 Read the whole piece carefully, thinking about the **facts**.
3 Note down the **main points**, leaving out the examples and unimportant information.
4 Write the **summary** from your **notes** (not from the original text); your writing should make sense on its own.
5 Count the number of words you have used. If you have more than 80 words, you have probably included something unimportant. If you have less than 70, you might have left out something important.

Here your child learns to summarise a piece of text in a specified number of words. Your child's summary needs to include all the main points from the passage and to make sense on its own. Help your child to follow the guidelines.

Analysing text

How **effective** is the **historical information** about pirates on page 22? The following questions will help you **analyse** the writer's text.

How effective is the **introduction**? (How well does it get across its message?)

....

....

How effective is the main part of the piece? For example, does it give you enough **information**? Is it easy to understand?

....

....

....

Does the writer express her own **opinion** of pirates? Write down her **opinion**.

....

....

Now design a "Wanted" **poster** for any pirate you wish – either real or imaginary. Provide a **description** of the pirate's crimes. Draw a **picture** of him or her (there were several notorious women pirates), and offer a good reward.

These exercises are designed to encourage your child to think about the pirate text. Explain to your child that there are no right or wrong answers to these sorts of questions. Any answer that can be sensibly arrived at from the text is acceptable.

Reading a classic novel

Woodes Rogers, the governor who cleared the Bahamas of pirates, discovered a castaway ex-pirate called Alexander Selkirk on the Juan Fernandez Islands. Parts of Selkirk's story were later used by Daniel Defoe in his famous book, *Robinson Crusoe*. Here is the opening paragraph of *Robinson Crusoe*.

I was born in the year 1632, in the city of York, of a good family, though not of that country, my father being a foreigner of Bremen who settled first at Hull. He got a good estate by merchandise and, leaving off his trade, lived afterward at York, from whence he had married my mother, whose relations were named Robinson, a very good family in that country, and from whom I was called Robinson Kreutznaer; but by the usual corruption of words in England we are now called, nay, we call ourselves, and write our name "Crusoe," and so my companions always called me.

Read carefully through the paragraph, thinking of **modern** words and phrases that could be used instead of those used by Daniel Defoe. Now **rewrite** the paragraph in **modern English**. Try to include the same information.

....

....

....

....

....

....

....

....

....

....

....

....

....

....

This writing activity provides further practice in recognising archaic expressions and replacing them with modern equivalents. You may need to help your child with this. The retelling should contain all the main points from the original.

Writing a journal

In the book *Robinson Crusoe*, Robinson writes a **journal** to record what happens to him after he is shipwrecked on an island. Read this **extract** from the book, then answer the question that follows.

> **September 30, 1659.** I, poor, miserable Robinson Crusoe, being shipwrecked, during a dreadful storm in the offing, came on shore on this dismal unfortunate island, which I called "the Island of Despair," all the rest of the ship's company being drowned, and myself almost dead.
>
> All the rest of that day I spent in afflicting myself at the dismal circumstances I was brought to, viz., I had neither food, house, clothes, weapon, or place to fly to, and in despair of any relief, saw nothing but death before me, either that I should be devoured by wild beasts, murdered by savages, or starved to death for want of food. At the approach of night, I slept in a tree for fear of wild creatures, but slept soundly, though it rained all night.
>
> **October 1.** In the morning I saw to my great surprise, the ship had floated with the high tide and was driven on shore again much nearer the island, which, as it was some comfort on one hand (for seeing her sit upright and not broken to pieces, I hoped, if the wind abated, I might get on board …

What do you think Robinson plans to do next? Write some brief **notes** of your ideas.

....

....

....

....

....

....

Copy the beginning of the entry for October 1 onto a separate sheet of paper. Use your best **joined handwriting**. Then continue the **journal** for rest of the day. Use the **notes** that you wrote above to help you plan the entry. Try to write it as if you were Robinson Crusoe, using some **old-fashioned words** where you can.

The task here is to write a continuation of a famous story in a similarly "old-fashioned" style and in the same form as the original – a diary written in the first person. Encourage your child to read his or her completed journal entry to you.

Writing a script

Pirates feature in many popular stories. Pirate characters have also appeared on stage, in film and on television. Now it's your turn to write a **scene** for film or television with a pirate as the main character. You can use an incident from a well-known story, such as *Peter Pan* or *Treasure Island*, or you can make up your own.

This **planning sheet** will help you to get started. Make brief **notes** only.

Setting – time and place (Will the scene take place in the past, present or future? Is it set on Earth or elsewhere?)

....

....

Characters – about three or four only (Who are your characters? How will you interest your audience in them?)

....

....

Plot – what happens (What events or action take place?)

....

....

....

....

....

Write your **script** on a separate sheet of paper. Before you write, you will need to have a clear idea of what happens at the **beginning** and **end** of your scene. Also remember to give directions for the camera and for the characters' actions. Write the dialogue next to the characters' names (without speech marks).

On this page your child learns to write a play script. Check that your child understands the difference between a play script and a story: a play script has no narrator and the emphasis should be on dialogue.

Writing a news report

Imagine that you are the space correspondent for the *Intergalactic Times*. You receive this hurried SOS e-mail from far away in the universe.

> **SOS**
> strange silent black craft locked onto starboard wing area   white markings skull and crossbones! sounds of hatch opening   who are they it's …

At this point the e-mail ends abruptly, and you have to interpret the message. Use this "electronic notepad" to write quick **notes**.

Now decide on your **headline**, and write it here. Use a separate sheet of paper to write your **report** and to warn your readers of the danger.

INTERGALACTIC TIMES

These activities provide practice in two areas: journalistic writing and the modern adaptation of traditional stories and themes. Your child's writing should read like a newspaper report and fulfil the brief. Remember to praise his or her achievements.

Reading poetry

Read this **poem** aloud, then answer the questions that follow.
Helpful hint: As you read the poem, remember that the poet lives in a country where November is a cold month in early winter.

November

No sun, no moon,
No morn, no noon,
No dawn, no dusk, no proper time of day;
No sky, no earthly view,
No distance looking blue.

No road, no street, no t'other side the way;
No end to any row,
No indications where the crescents go,
No top to any steeple,
No recognition of familiar people,
No courtesies for showing them,
No knowing them,
No travelling at all, no locomotion,
No inkling of the way, no notion,
No go by land or ocean,
No mail, no post,
No news from any foreign coast,
No park, no ring, no afternoon gentility,
No company, no nobility,

No warmth, no cheerfulness, no healthful ease,
No comfortable feel in any member,
No shade, no shine, no butterflies, no bees,
No fruits, no flowers, no leaves, no trees:
November!

Thomas Hood

Why does the poet feel that there is nothing to see or do? Describe his **mood**.
It is foggy so the poet can't see familiar things. Possibly the bad weather
has kept everyone inside so he is bored and unhappy.

In your **opinion**, is this a balanced view of November? Give reasons for your answer.
....
Answers may vary

Here your child is analysing persuasive writing and the writer's viewpoint. Make sure your child makes the connection between the use of the word *no* throughout the poem and the fact that the word *November* begins with the letters *n* and *o*.

Understanding poetry

Reread the **poem** on page 28, then answer the following questions.

What does the word **dialect** mean? Find an example of a **dialect phrase** in the **poem**. Write it down with its meaning. [D]
A dialect is a form of a language spoken in a particular region.
"t'other side the way" means "the other side of the road".

Explain these words as used in the **poem**: crescents, courtesies, gentility, inkling. [D]
Crescents are curved streets. Courtesies are greetings and polite remarks.
Gentility means polite company. Inkling means idea.

Would you describe this **poem** as funny, serious or both? Explain your answer.
Answers may vary

Describe the **patterns** that you can see and hear in this poem. Look for **patterns** in the rhyme, rhythm and alliteration, and in the sounds of words and phrases.
Answers may vary

Look back to page 2 to find the real **origin**, or meaning, of the word **November**. The **poem** on page 28 implies the word **November** has another meaning, what is it? (Hint: **No**-vember)
This poem implies that November means the month of "no", that it is the
month when nothing happens.

Would you include this **poem** in a **brochure** aimed at attracting tourists? If not, why not?
No it does not give a positive view of November where the poet lives.

These questions provide practice in examining the vocabulary and rhythms found in poetry. You may need to make suggestions to help your child with some of the answers. Check that your child writes his or her answers in complete sentences.

More poetry

Read this **poem** aloud. As you read, remember that the poet lives in a country where December is a cold winter month.

December

Does the
Dreary,
Dull,
December drizzle get
Deep into your
Daydreams – or
Do you remember the
Daily
Delights of long, languid summer
Days?

John Hesk

In southern-hemisphere countries, such as Australia, December is a hot month in early summer. Write a **poem** about December in the southern hemisphere. Try to start each line with the letter D. Make your **poem** 10 lines long. (Can you think of a reason for this?) It is up to you whether or not you use **rhyme** or a **regular rhythm** in your **poem**.

Answers may vary

On this page the task is for your child to write a poem. Suggest that your child tries to continue the sense through the lines, as in the example. Encourage your child to read his or her finished poem out loud, and be sure to praise it.

An acrostic poem

This poem has an **acrostic** pattern. As you read it, see if you can work out what this means.

Winter

When water is freezing
I seldom stop sneezing.
Numbing my nose;
Tingling my toes.
Emergency heat;
Required for the feet.

John Hesk

An **acrostic poem** about Spring would be six lines long, like the poem above. Why is this?
There are six letters in the word "spring". Each line of the poem would begin
with one of the letters in the word "spring".

Now write an **acrostic poem** about Spring. Decide whether or not you will use **rhyme** or **regular rhythm**. Practise your best, neatly spaced **joined handwriting**. You might like to decorate or illustrate your **poem**.

S .....
P .....
R .....
I .....
N .....
G .....

Answers may vary

Here your child learns to write a poem following the set pattern of an acrostic. Again, the poem will work best if the sense continues from line to line. Encourage your child to start some of the lines with words other than nouns.

Jumbled letters

The first **syllables** in these three-syllable words have been **interchanged** (swapped) with one another. Look carefully at the nonsense words, then match each beginning with its proper ending. Check the spelling of each word in a **dictionary** before you write it down. The first one has been done for you. [D]
Remember: A **syllable** is a word or part of a word that is one beat long.

passdener passenger
wondkerchief wonderful
umplanation umbrella
goviful government
courhaviour courageous
exbrella explanation
beageous behaviour
prodience procession
aucession audience
piterment pitiful
inqueror incredible
handerful handkerchief
garenger gardener
concredible conqueror

The letters in the words below are completely jumbled. When correctly spelled, each word is the name of a country. Time yourself to see how long it will take to sort them out.

ACHIN China   HELIC Chile
YALTI Italy   ANIDI India
RASTUILAA Australia MANGERY Germany
EXIMOC Mexico   ROWANY Norway

These activities help your child with difficult spellings by encouraging him or her to look closely at combinations of letters and to remember the patterns. If your child finds the country names difficult, try giving the initial letters as clues.

A writer's style

Read the following **description**, then answer the questions.

> ... I can remember exactly what was on the table that evening. It was my favourite thing of all, toad-in-the-hole, and my mum could make toad-in-the-hole like nobody else in the world. She did it in an enormous pan with the Yorkshire pudding very brown and crisp on top and raised up in huge bubbly mountains. In between the mountains you could see the sausages half-buried in the batter. Fantastic it was.
>
> From *Danny, Champion of the World* by Roald Dahl

What is **toad-in-the-hole**? Why do you think the writer chose this type of meal? D

....

....

Make a list of the **exaggerated expressions** used in this description.

....

....

Can you find a **metaphor** that reminds you of the Norwegian feast on page 16?

....

How might you know that Roald Dahl wrote this? Look at the **style** of writing, and compare it with the **style** of the text on page 16.
Remember: An author's **style** is the particular way in which he or she writes.

....

....

Fact or fiction?

Find these words in a **dictionary**, then write your own **definition** of each. ☐D

biography ....

autobiography ....

Look back at page 14. Is *Jane Eyre* a **factual** or **fictional autobiography**? Give a reason for your answer.

....

....

Is *Jane Eyre* written in the **first person** (using **I/we**) or the **third person** (using **she/they**)?

....

Do you think the **description** on page 16 is from a **factual** or **fictional autobiography**? Give a reason for your answer.

....

....

How would you describe your writing about Shakespeare on page 6?

....

....

Write your own **description** of your favourite meal (either real or imaginary) as Roald Dahl might have written it. First, reread the texts on pages 16 and 17 to get a feel for Dahl's **style**, then use this menu card as a **plan**.

M E N U

Starter: ....

....

Main course: ....

....

Dessert: ....

....

Now write the **description** on a separate sheet of paper. Try to use the same **style** as Roald Dahl, but use your own **similes** and **metaphors**.

18

Limericks

Read the following **limericks**, then answer the questions.

1   Asks Paolo, when peckish, in Pisa,
    "Spaghetti and sauce – what is eas*ia*?"
    Each evening at eight
    He sits down to a plate
    Of the most perfect pasta in Pisa.

3   Dolores, down Mexico way,
    Likes chilli con carne each day.
    That the chillis are hot
    Troubles her not one jot!
    She just chooses her chilli that way.

    2   Now, Mamie and Max from Manhattan
        Think doughnuts are great – but they fatten!
        All sticky and sweet,
        Only bought for a treat,
        Just the food for a "mood" in Manhattan.

Glenis Hesk

Do you know why poems like these are called **limericks**? Try to find out, then look at the **limericks** above to help you complete this **definition**. ☐D

A limerick is a comic verse that always has ___ ___ ___ ___ lines. The longer lines,

which are lines one, ___ ___ ___ and ___ ___ ___ ___, rhyme with each other.

The ___ ___ ___ ___ ___ ___ ___ lines, three and ___ ___ ___ ___, share a different rhyme.

This rhyme **pattern**, or rhyme **scheme**, is known as A, A, B, B, A.

How many examples of **alliteration** can you find in the first **limerick**? ....
Can you explain the meaning of **alliteration**?

....

....

Write the words that **alliterate** in the second and the third **limericks**.

....

....

Which extra two **rhyming words** in the second **limerick** are not in the expected place at
the ends of the lines?

....

Did you notice the "funny" spelling in the first **limerick**? Why do you think it is there?

....

What does the saying "not one jot" mean?

....

Alliteration

Write down any four words that **alliterate** with **chooses** and **chilli**.
Remember: **Alliteration** is when two or more words close to each other in a piece of writing begin with the same sound.

....

Now write down **two** words that **alliterate** with each of the following words. Use the sound made by the **two** letters at the beginning of the words.

what .... think ....

treat .... sticky ....

sweet .... fleet ....

brand .... flavour ....

shoulder .... phantom ....

quarter .... wrinkle ....

Now use the sound of the **three** letters at the beginning of each of these words to write **three** more words that **alliterate** with each one.

thread ....

stranger ....

splendid ....

sprout ....

scramble ....

squash ....

chrome ....

Writing limericks

Try writing some **limericks** of your own on any **subject** or **theme**. Use what you have learned on pages 19 and 20 to help you. Remember to make your limericks **amusing**.

....

....

....

....

....

                    ....

                    ....

                    ....

                    ....

                    ....

....

....

....

....

                    ....

                    ....

                    ....

                    ....

Reading and understanding

Although pirates in stories are often portrayed as lovable rogues, the real-life pirates who sailed the oceans searching out laden ships were usually ruthless robbers. Read the following **historical information** about real pirates.

The Bahamas pirates became so cocksure that in 1718, when the British government sent a fleet of ships to clear the islands of piracy, one of them – Charles Vane – sailed down the line of naval vessels saluting each one.

That same year, however, a new governor arrived who at last succeeded in clearing the Bahamas of pirates. He was Woodes Rogers, originally a merchant from Bristol, and himself a former pirate. Between 1708 and 1711 Rogers made a privateering voyage to make up for the losses he had suffered when pirates seized his ships. Rogers looted the Spanish colony at Guayaquil, Ecuador, where he stole a fortune in silver and valuables. On his way home to England he captured a Spanish galleon with treasure on board worth £1 million.

As governor, Rogers dealt with the Bahamas pirates by first offering them a pardon. Some accepted. Those who did not were very severely dealt with. In November 1718 Rogers had three captured pirates put on trial, followed by ten more in December.

From then on the 2,000 pirates still at large in the Caribbean avoided the Bahamas. As for Charles Vane, he accepted the pardon Rogers offered, but wanted to keep all his ill-gotten gains. When Rogers refused, Vane hoisted the "Jolly Roger," fired one last defiant salvo, and sailed away. He was never seen in the Bahamas again.

From *World History* by Brenda Ralph Lewis

Now **summarise** (write a shortened version of) this extract. Use a separate sheet of paper, and try to write no more than 80 words. Here are some guidelines to help you.

1 Read the first sentence, think about it, then read the last sentence.
2 Read the whole piece carefully, thinking about the **facts**.
3 Note down the **main points**, leaving out the examples and unimportant information.
4 Write the **summary** from your **notes** (not from the original text); your writing should make sense on its own.
5 Count the number of words you have used. If you have more than 80 words, you have probably included something unimportant. If you have less than 70, you might have left out something important.

Analysing text

How **effective** is the **historical information** about pirates on page 22?
The following questions will help you **analyse** the writer's text.

How effective is the **introduction**? (How well does it get across its message?)

....

....

How effective is the main part of the piece? For example, does it give you enough
information? Is it easy to understand?

....

....

Does the writer express a clear **opinion** of pirates? Write down her **opinion**.

....

....

Now design a "Wanted" **poster** for any pirate you wish – either real or imaginary.
Provide a **description** of the pirate's crimes. Draw a **picture** of him or her (there were
several notorious women pirates), and offer a good reward.

Reading a classic novel

Woodes Rogers, the governor who cleared the Bahamas of pirates, discovered a castaway ex-pirate called Alexander Selkirk on the Juan Fernandez Islands. Parts of Selkirk's story were later used by Daniel Defoe in his famous book, *Robinson Crusoe*. Here is the opening paragraph of *Robinson Crusoe*.

I was born in the year 1632, in the city of York, of a good family, though not of that country, my father being a foreigner of Bremen who settled first at Hull. He got a good estate by merchandise and, leaving off his trade, lived afterward at York, from whence he had married my mother, whose relations were named Robinson, a very good family in that country, and from whom I was called Robinson Kreutznaer; but by the usual corruption of words in England we are now called, nay, we call ourselves, and write our name "Crusoe," and so my companions always called me.

Read carefully through the paragraph, thinking of **modern** words and phrases that could be used instead of those used by Daniel Defoe. Now **rewrite** the paragraph in **modern English**. Try to include the same information.

....
....
....
....
....
....
....
....
....
....
....
....

Writing a journal

In the book *Robinson Crusoe*, Robinson writes a **journal** to record what happens to him after he is shipwrecked on an island. Read this **extract** from the book, then answer the question that follows.

September 30, 1659. I, poor, miserable Robinson Crusoe, being shipwrecked, during a dreadful storm in the offing, came on shore on this dismal unfortunate island, which I called "the Island of Despair," all the rest of the ship's company being drowned, and myself almost dead.

All the rest of that day I spent in afflicting myself at the dismal circumstances I was brought to, viz., I had neither food, house, clothes, weapon, or place to fly to, and in despair of any relief, saw nothing but death before me, either that I should be devoured by wild beasts, murdered by savages, or starved to death for want of food. At the approach of night, I slept in a tree for fear of wild creatures, but slept soundly, though it rained all night.

October 1. In the morning I saw to my great surprise, the ship had floated with the high tide and was driven on shore again much nearer the island, which, as it was some comfort on one hand (for seeing her sit upright and not broken to pieces, I hoped, if the wind abated, I might get on board …

What do you think Robinson plans to do next? Write some brief **notes** of your ideas.

....

....

....

....

....

....

....

Copy the beginning of the entry for October 1 onto a separate sheet of paper. Use your best **joined handwriting**. Then continue the **journal** for rest of the day. Use the **notes** that you wrote above to help you plan the entry. Try to write it as if you were Robinson Crusoe, using some **old-fashioned words** where you can.

Writing a script

Pirates feature in many popular stories. Pirate characters have also appeared on stage, in film and on television. Now it's your turn to write a **scene** for film or television with a pirate as the main character. You can use an incident from a well-known story, such as *Peter Pan* or *Treasure Island*, or you can make up your own.

This **planning sheet** will help you to get started. Make brief **notes** only.

Setting – time and place (Will the scene take place in the past, present or future? Is it set on Earth or elsewhere?)

....

....

Characters – about three or four only (Who are your characters? How will you interest your audience in them?)

....

....

Plot – what happens (What events or actions take place?)

....

....

....

....

....

....

....

Write your **script** on a separate sheet of paper. Before you write, you will need to have a clear idea of what happens at the **beginning** and **end** of your **scene**. Also remember to give directions for the camera and for the characters' actions. Write the dialogue next to the characters' names (without speech marks).

Writing a news report

Imagine that you are the space correspondent for the *Intergalactic Times*. You receive this hurried SOS e-mail from far away in the universe.

SOS
strange silent black craft locked onto starboard
wing area   white markings skull and crossbones!
sounds of hatch opening   who are they it's …

At this point the e-mail ends abruptly, and you have to interpret the message. Use this "electronic notepad" to write quick **notes**.

Now decide on your **headline**, and write it here. Use a separate sheet of paper to write your **report** and to warn your readers of the danger.

INTERGALACTIC TIMES

Reading poetry

Read this **poem** aloud, then answer the questions that follow.
Helpful hint: As you read the poem, remember that the poet lives in a country where November is a cold month in early winter.

November

No sun, no moon,
No morn, no noon,
No dawn, no dusk, no proper time of day;
No sky, no earthly view,
No distance looking blue.

No road, no street, no t'other side the way;
No end to any row,
No indications where the crescents go,
No top to any steeple,
No recognition of familiar people,
No courtesies for showing them,
No knowing them,
No travelling at all, no locomotion,
No inkling of the way, no notion,
No go by land or ocean,
No mail, no post,
No news from any foreign coast,
No park, no ring, no afternoon gentility,
No company, no nobility,

No warmth, no cheerfulness, no healthful ease,
No comfortable feel in any member,
No shade, no shine, no butterflies, no bees,
No fruits, no flowers, no leaves, no trees:
November!

Thomas Hood

Why does the poet feel that there is nothing to see or do? Describe his **mood**.

....

....

In your **opinion**, is this a balanced view of November? Give reasons for your answer.

....

....

Understanding poetry

Reread the **poem** on page 28, then answer the following questions.

What does the word **dialect** mean? Find an example of a **dialect phrase** in the **poem**. Write it down with its meaning. D

....

....

Explain these words as used in the **poem**: crescents, courtesies, gentility, inkling. D

....

....

....

....

Would you describe this **poem** as funny, serious or both? Explain your answer.

....

....

Describe the **patterns** that you can see and hear in this **poem**. Look for **patterns** in the rhyme, rhythm and alliteration, and in the sounds of words and phrases.

....

....

....

Look back to page 2 to find the real **origin**, or meaning, of the word **November**. The **poem** on page 28 implies the word **November** has another meaning, what is it? (Hint: **No**-vember)

....

....

Would you include this **poem** in a **brochure** aimed at attracting tourists? If not, why not?

....

....

More poetry

Read this **poem** aloud. As you read, remember that the poet lives in a country where December is a cold winter month.

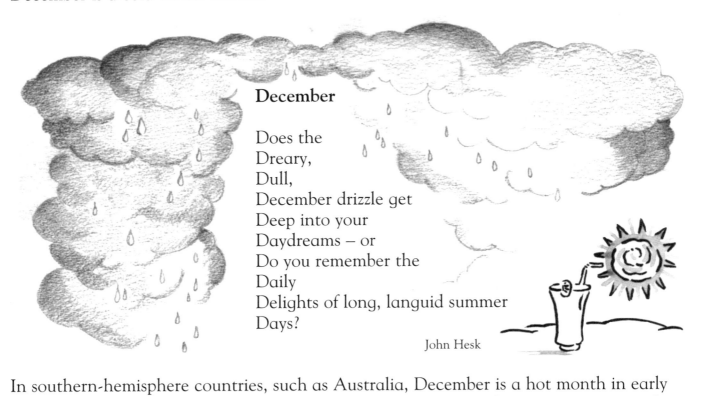

December

Does the
Dreary,
Dull,
December drizzle get
Deep into your
Daydreams – or
Do you remember the
Daily
Delights of long, languid summer
Days?

John Hesk

In southern-hemisphere countries, such as Australia, December is a hot month in early summer. Write a **poem** about December in the southern hemisphere. Try to start each line with the letter D. Make your **poem** 10 lines long. (Can you think of a reason for this?) It is up to you whether or not you use **rhyme** or a **regular rhythm** in your **poem**.

....

....

....

....

....

....

....

....

An acrostic poem

This poem has an **acrostic** pattern. As you read it, see if you can work out what this means.

Winter

When water is freezing
I seldom stop sneezing.
Numbing my nose;
Tingling my toes.
Emergency heat;
Required for the feet.

John Hesk

An **acrostic poem** about Spring would be six lines long, like the poem above. Why is this?

....

....

Now write an **acrostic poem** about Spring. Decide whether or not you will use **rhyme** or **regular rhythm**. Practise your best, neatly spaced **joined handwriting**. You might like to decorate or illustrate your **poem**.

S ....

P ....

R ....

I ....

N ....

G ....

Jumbled letters

The first **syllables** in these three-syllable words have been **interchanged** (swapped) with one another. Look carefully at the nonsense words, then match each beginning with its proper ending. Check the spelling of each word in a **dictionary** before you write it down. The first one has been done for you. $\boxed{D}$

Remember: A **syllable** is a word or part of a word that is one beat long.

passdener *passenger* ....

wondkerchief ....

umplanation ....

goviful ....

courhaviour ....

exbrella ....

beageous ....

prodience ....

aucession ....

piternment ....

inqueror ....

handerful ....

garenger ....

concredible...

The letters in the words below are completely jumbled. When correctly spelled, each word is the name of a country. Time yourself to see how long it will take to sort them out.

ACHIN .... HELIC ....

YALTI .... ANIDI ....

RASTUILAA............................... MANGERY ....

EXIMOC .... ROWANY ....